I can play that!

Lena Eckhoff

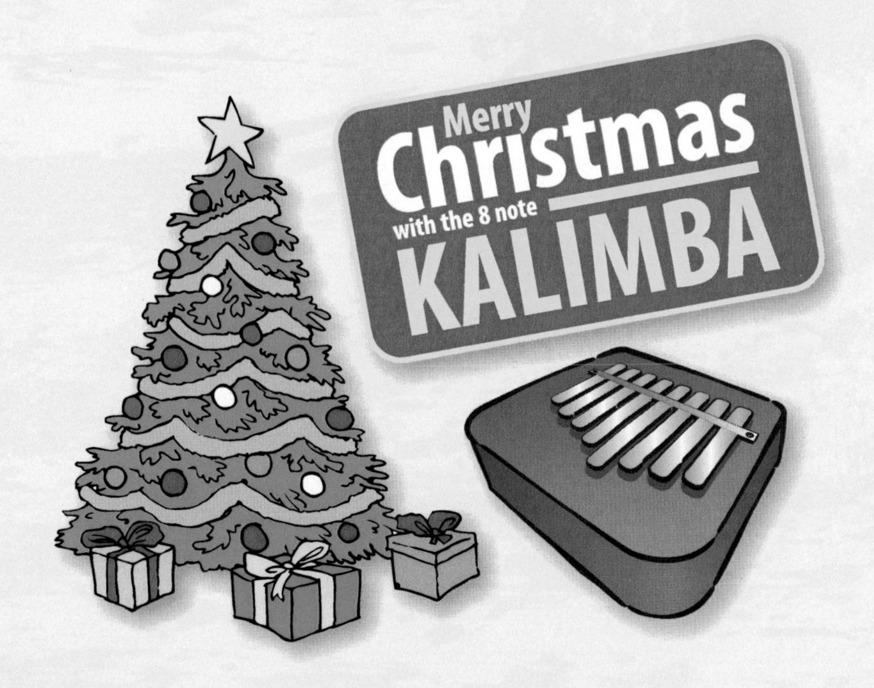
Merry
Christmas
with the 8 note
KALIMBA

Lena Eckh
I can play t
Merry Christmas with th
Cover picture: © Sergey No

le.eckhoff@gmail.com

ISBN: 9798494632456

Welcome!

The 8 key kalimba is ideally suited for kids and beginners, sharing the layout with its larger siblings, but with less notes to worry about. And the graphic notation used in this book makes it even easier–you'll play your first song in a short few minutes without having to read a single note!

Just pick up your kalimba and follow the numbers–it's as easy as that!
If you'd rather play by colors, simply cut out the labels on the last page and fix them to your kalimba using a small piece of adhesive tape.

> ! The songs in this book **can not** be played on **pentatonic** kalimbas (models missing the numbers 4 and 7).

You only need these notes to play the songs in this book:

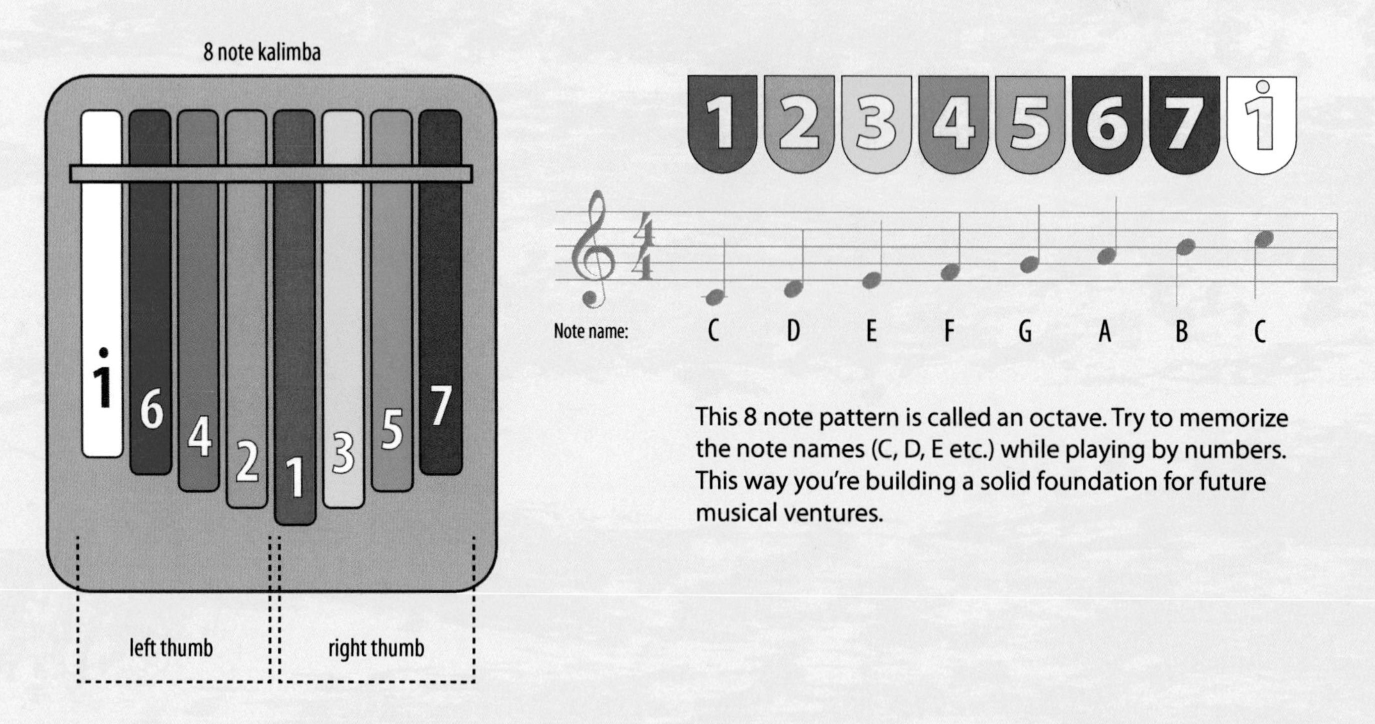
8 note kalimba
i 6 4 2 1 3 5 7
left thumb
right thumb
1 2 3 4 5 6 7 i
Note name:
C D E F G A B C

This 8 note pattern is called an octave. Try to memorize the note names (C, D, E etc.) while playing by numbers. This way you're building a solid foundation for future musical ventures.

Please note: This book is written for **8 note diatonic kalimba models**. Because it has the same layout as the bigger kalimba models, all songs can be played on models with 10 and 17 keys, too.

Songs

Christ was born on Christmas day

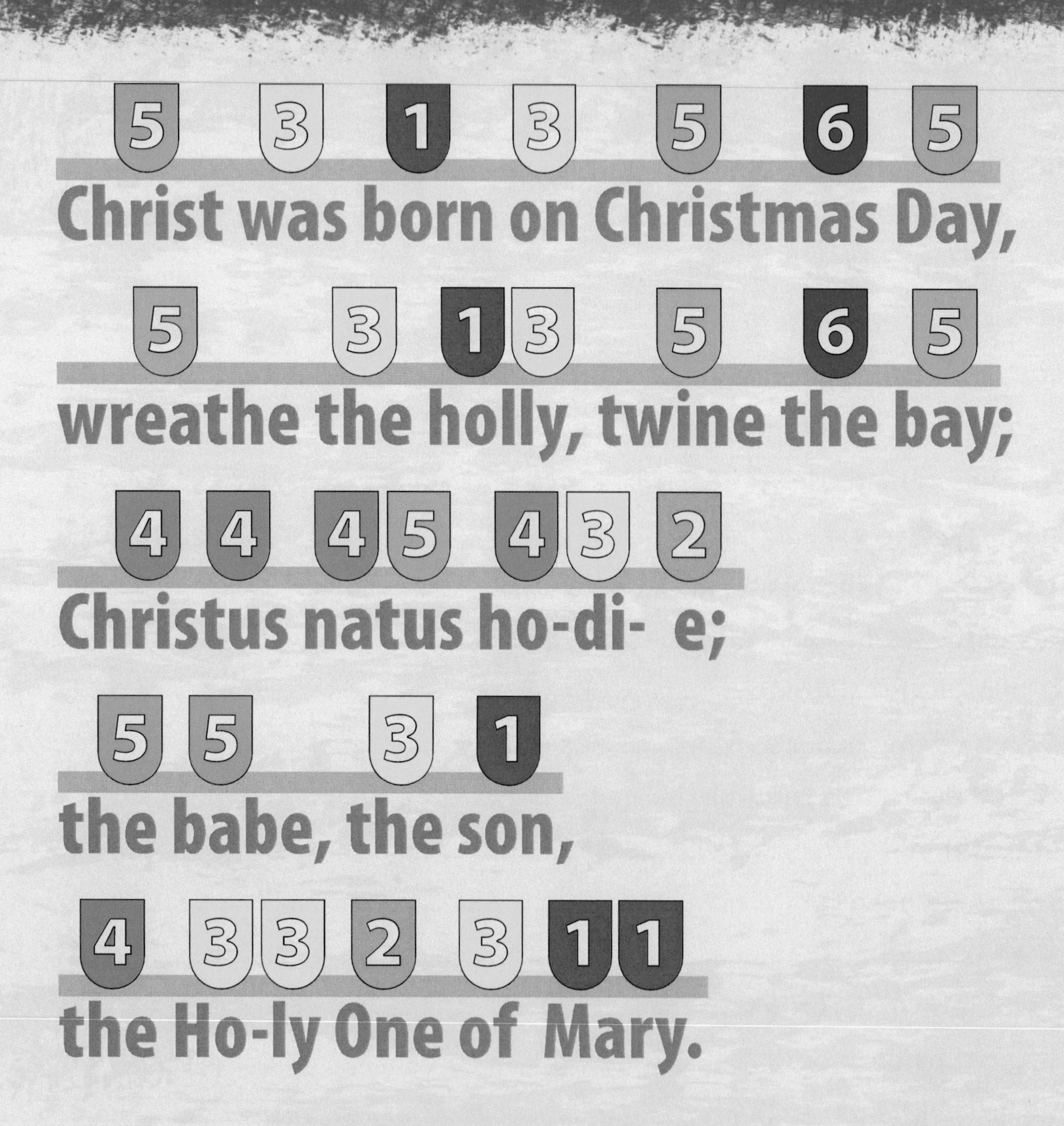
5 3 1 3 5 6 5
Christ was born on Christmas Day,
5 3 1 3 5 6 5
wreathe the holly, twine the bay;
4 4 4 5 4 3 2
Christus natus ho-di- e;
5 5 3 1
the babe, the son,
4 3 3 2 3 1 1
the Ho-ly One of Mary.

The boar's head carol

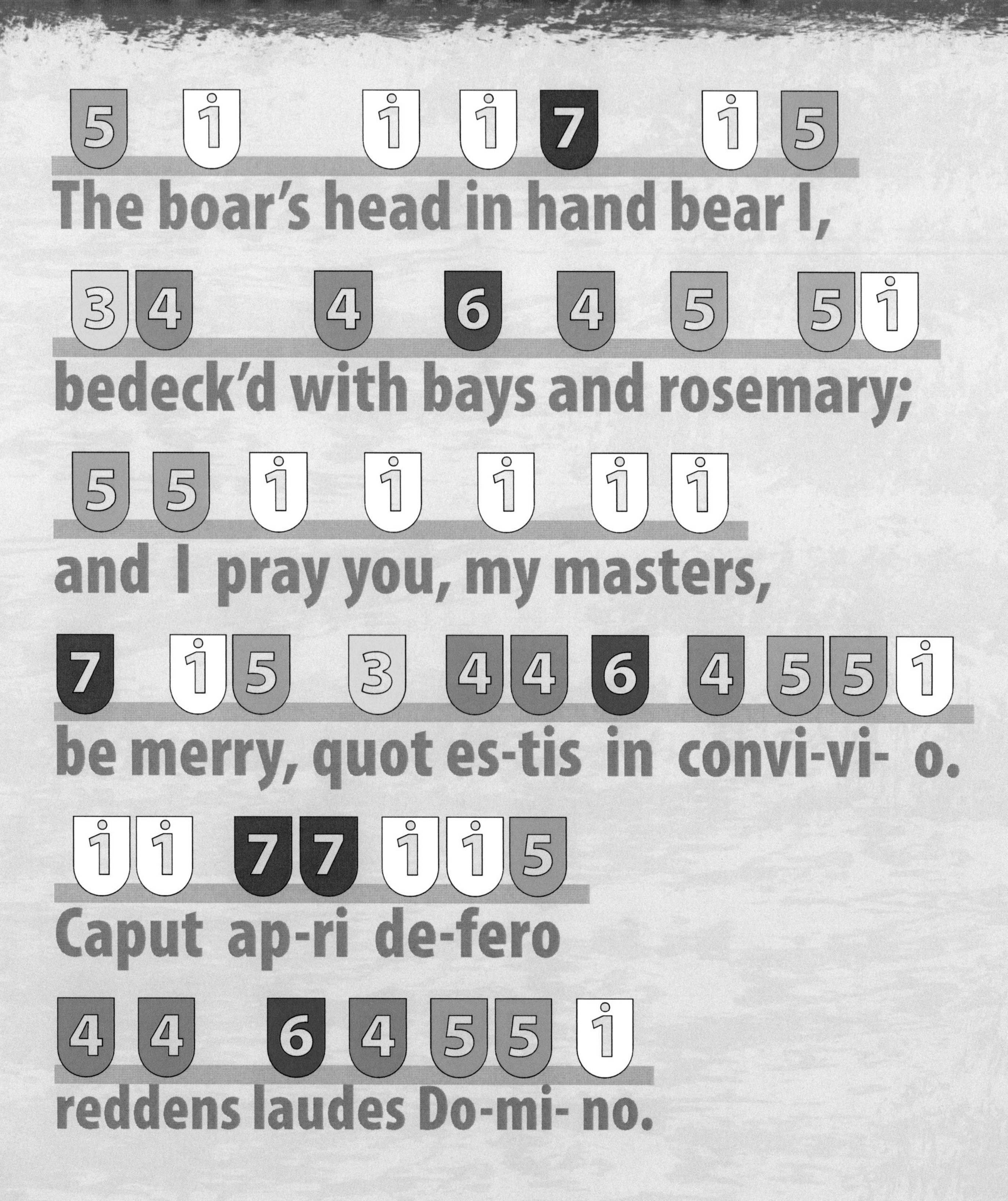
5 1̇ 1̇ 1̇ 7 1̇ 5
The boar's head in hand bear I,
3 4 4 6 4 5 5 1̇
bedeck'd with bays and rosemary;
5 5 1̇ 1̇ 1̇ 1̇ 1̇
and I pray you, my masters,
7 1̇ 5 3 4 4 6 4 5 5 1̇
be merry, quot es-tis in convi-vi- o.
1̇ 1̇ 7 7 1̇ 1̇ 5
Caput ap-ri de-fero
4 4 6 4 5 5 1̇
reddens laudes Do-mi- no.

Go, tell it on the mountain

7 7 6 5 3 2 5

Go, tell it on the mountain

6 6 5 6 5 6 7 5 3 2

over the hills and ev'rywhere.

7 7 6 5 3 2 5

Go, tell it on the mountain

1̇ 7 7 6 6 5

that Jesus Christ is born.

2 6 5 6 7 5

When I was a seeker

2 6 6 5 6 7

I sought both night and day.

2 6 6 5 6 7 5

I asked the Lord to help me

1̇ 7 5 6 6 5

and He showed me the way.

Jingle Bells

3 3 3 3 3 3

Jingle bells! Jingle bells!

3 5 1 2 3

Jingle all the way!

4 4 4 4 4 3 3

Oh, what fun it is to ride

3 3 2 2 3 2 5

a onehorse open sleigh!

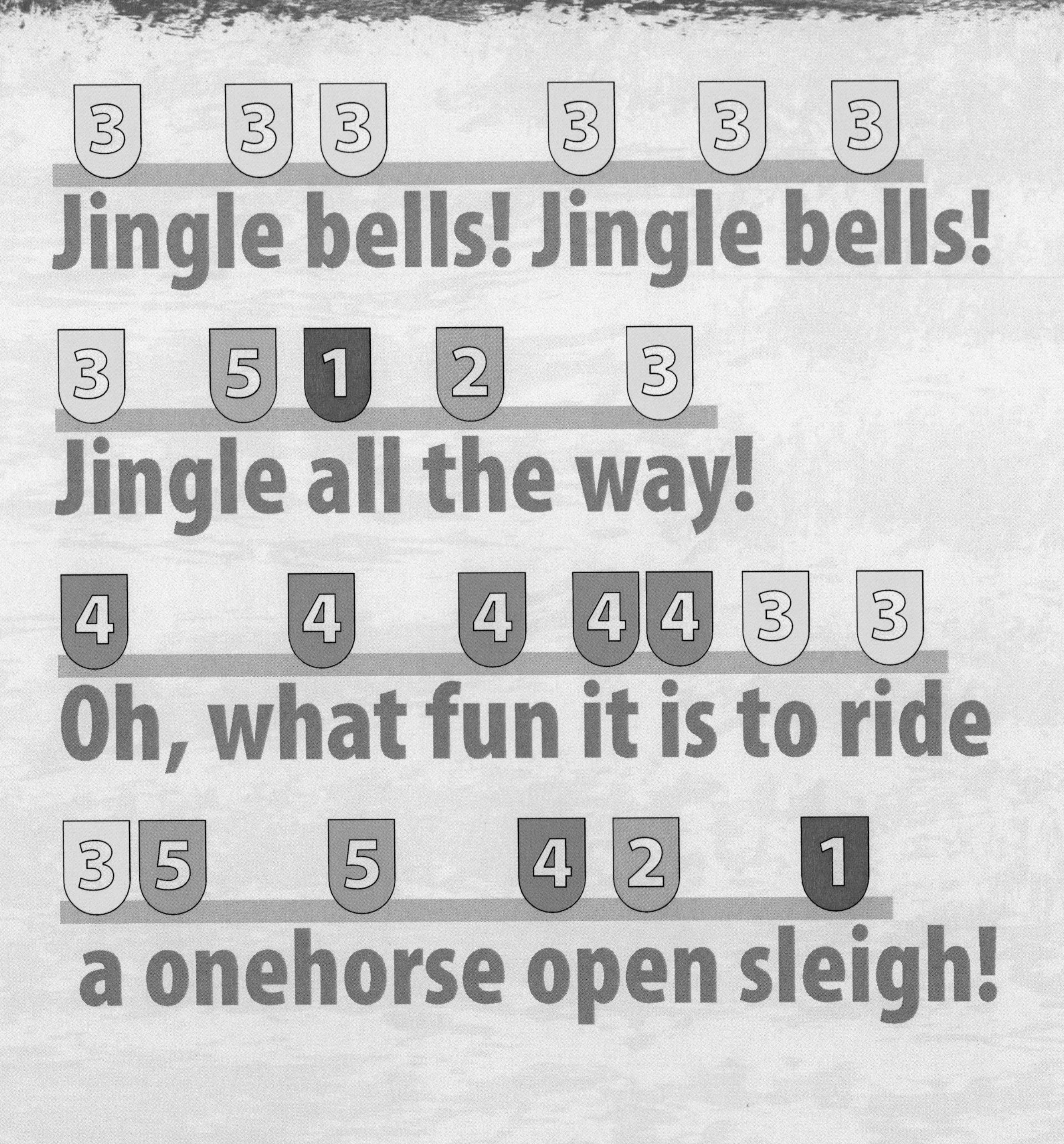
3 3 3 3 3 3
Jingle bells! Jingle bells!
3 5 1 2 3
Jingle all the way!
4 4 4 4 4 3 3
Oh, what fun it is to ride
3 5 5 4 2 1
a onehorse open sleigh!

The first Noel

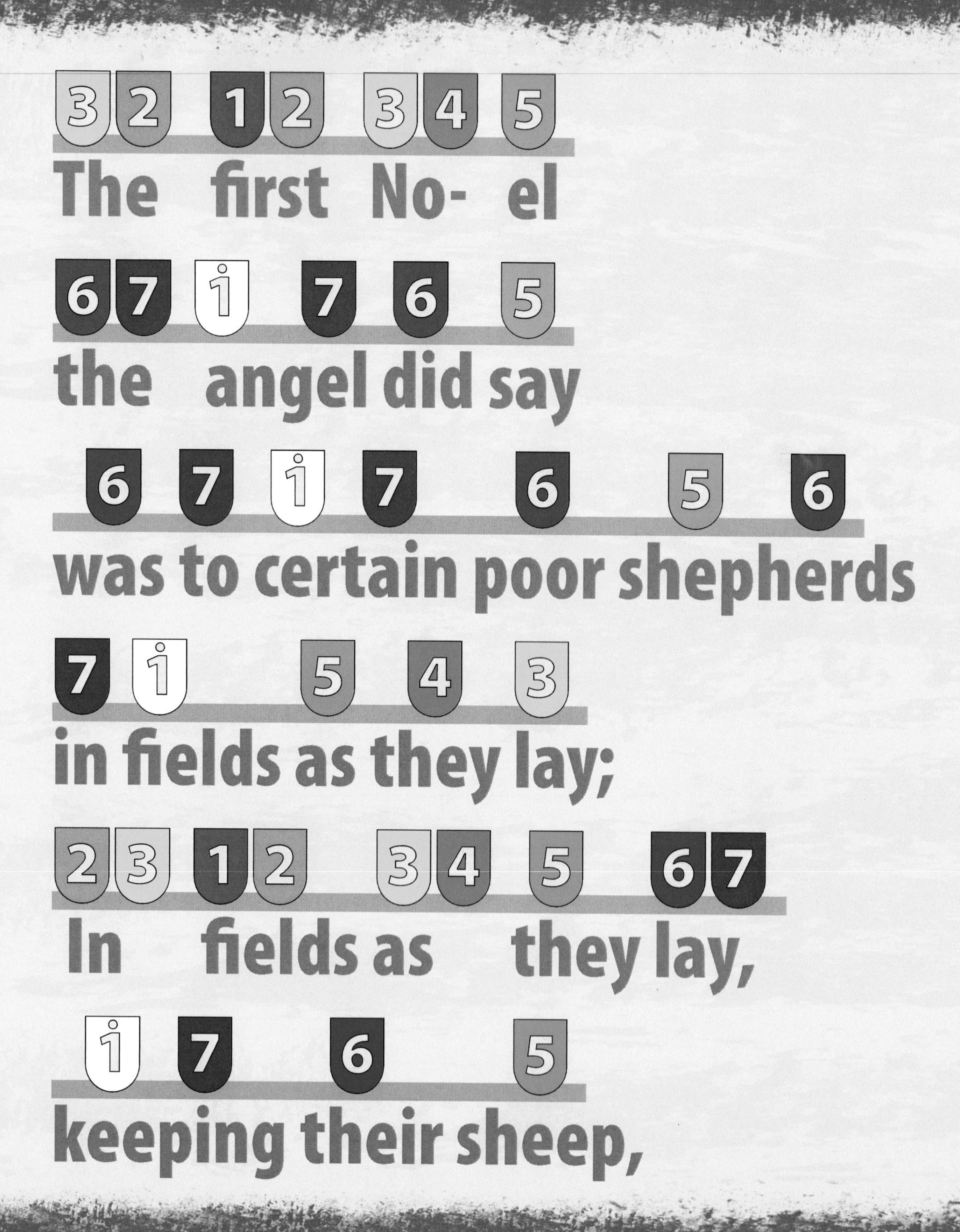
3 2 1 2 3 4 5
The first No- el
6 7 1̇ 7 6 5
the angel did say
6 7 1̇ 7 6 5 6
was to certain poor shepherds
7 1̇ 5 4 3
in fields as they lay;
2 3 1 2 3 4 5 6 7
In fields as they lay,
1̇ 7 6 5
keeping their sheep,

6 7 i̇ 7 6 5 6

on a cold winter's night

7 i̇ 5 4 3

that was so deep.

3 2 1 2 3 4 5

No- el, No- el,

i̇ 7 6 6 5

No- el, No-el,

i̇ 7 6 5 6 7 i̇ 5 4 3

born is the King of Is- ra-el!

Twinkle, twinkle, little star

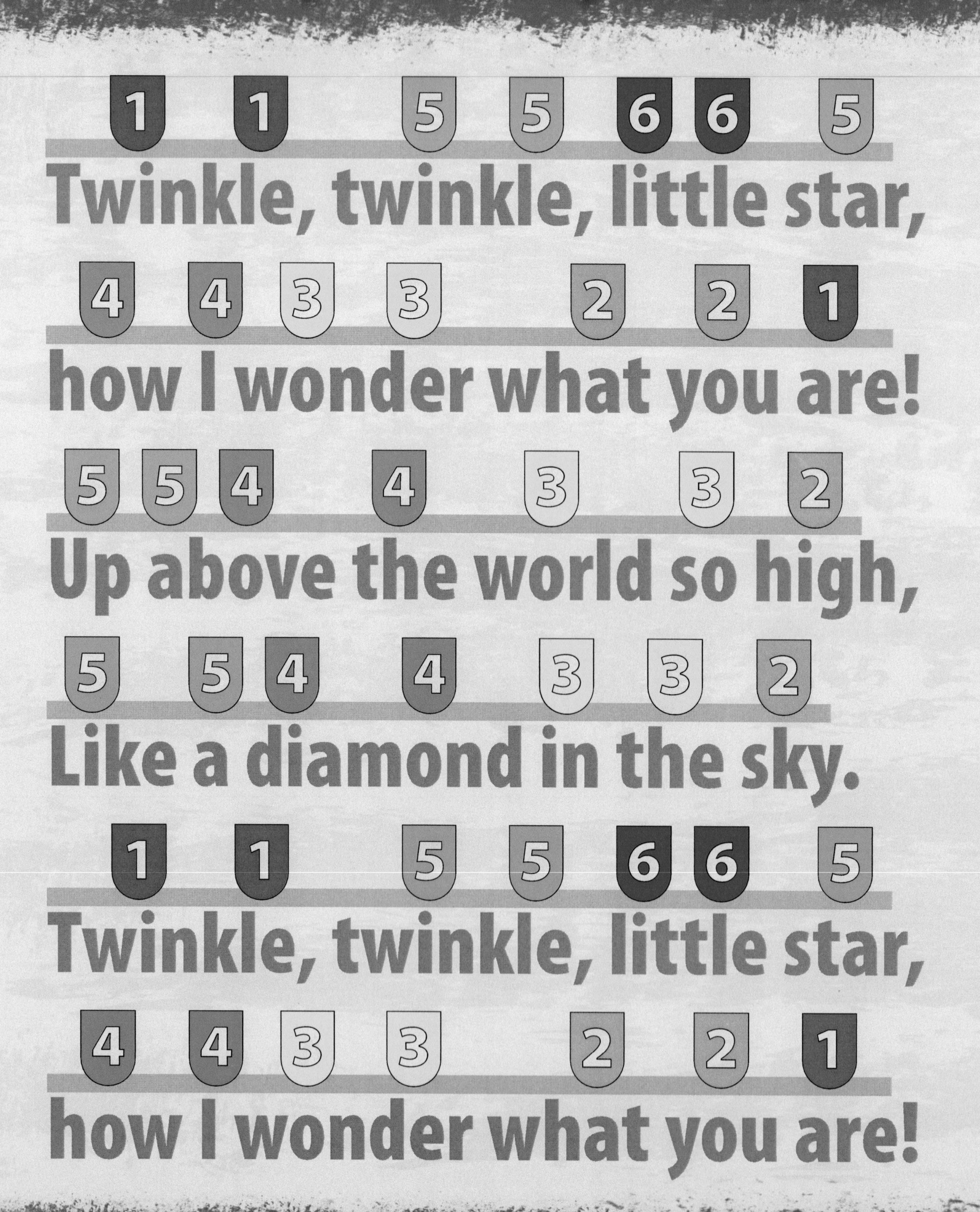

1 1 5 5 6 6 5
Twinkle, twinkle, little star,
4 4 3 3 2 2 1
how I wonder what you are!
5 5 4 4 3 3 2
Up above the world so high,
5 5 4 4 3 3 2
Like a diamond in the sky.
1 1 5 5 6 6 5
Twinkle, twinkle, little star,
4 4 3 3 2 2 1
how I wonder what you are!

I saw three ships

2 5 5 6 7 77 6
I saw three ships come sailing in

1̇ 7 5 5 7 6 6 2
on Christmas Day, on Christmas Day;

2 5 5 6 7 77 6
I saw three ships come sailing in

1̇ 7 5 56 7 6 5
on Christmas Day in the morning.

Up on the housetop

5 5 6 5 3 2 1 3 5

Up on the housetop reindeer pause,

6 6 5 3 2 5 5

out jumps good old Santa Claus.

5 5 6 5 3

Down through the chimney

2 1 3 5

with lots of toys,

6 6 6 5 5 3

all for the little ones'

2 5 1

Christmas joys.

4 4 6 5 5 5 3

Ho, ho, ho! Who wouldn't go!

2 4 4 3 5 5 1

Ho, ho, ho! Who wouldn't go!

5 5 6 5 3 4 5 6

Up on the housetop, click, click, click.

5 5 6 5 3

Down through the chimney

3 2 5 1

with good Saint Nick.

In the bleak midwinter

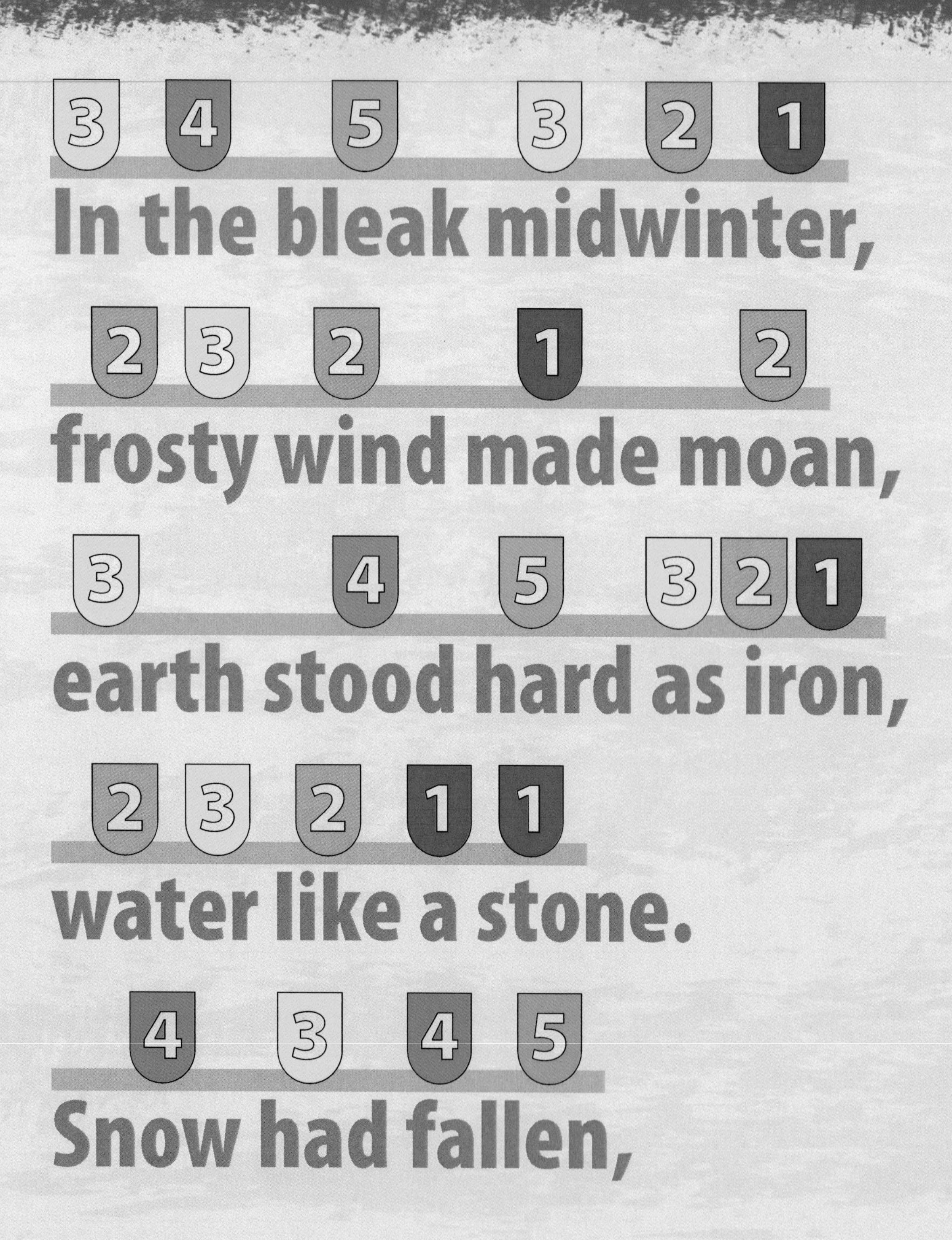
3 4 5 3 2 1
In the bleak midwinter,
2 3 2 1 2
frosty wind made moan,
3 4 5 3 2 1
earth stood hard as iron,
2 3 2 1 1
water like a stone.
4 3 4 5
Snow had fallen,

6 6 3

snow on snow,

5 3 2 1 2

snow on snow,

2 4 5 3 2 1

in the bleak midwinter,

2 3 2 1 1

long, long ago.

Joy to the world

$\dot{1}$ 7 6 5 4 3 2 1

Joy to the world, the Lord is come!

5 6 6 7 7 $\dot{1}$

Let earth receive her King;

$\dot{1}$ $\dot{1}$ 7 6 5 5 4 3

Let eve- ry heart

$\dot{1}$ $\dot{1}$ 7 6 5 5 4 3

prepare Him room

3 3 3 3 3 4 5

and heav'n and nature sing,

4 3 2 2 2 2 3 4

and heav'n and nature sing,

3 2 1 i̇ 6 5 4 3

and heav'n and hea- v'n

4 3 2 1

and nature sing.

Over the river and through the woods

5 5 5 5 3
O-ver the river
4 5 5 5
and through the woods
5 1̇ 1̇ 1̇ 7 6 5
to Grandmother's house we go.
5 4 4 4 4
The horse knows the way
4 3 3 3 3
to carry the sleigh
3 3 2
through the white

2 2 3 2 5
and drifted snow.

5 5 5 5 3
O-ver the river

4 5 5 5
and through the woods

5 i̇ i̇ 7 6 5
oh, how the wind does blow!

5 i̇ i̇ 7 6 5
It stings the toes and bites

3 1 2 3 3 4 3 2 1
the nose as over the ground we go.

Still, still, still

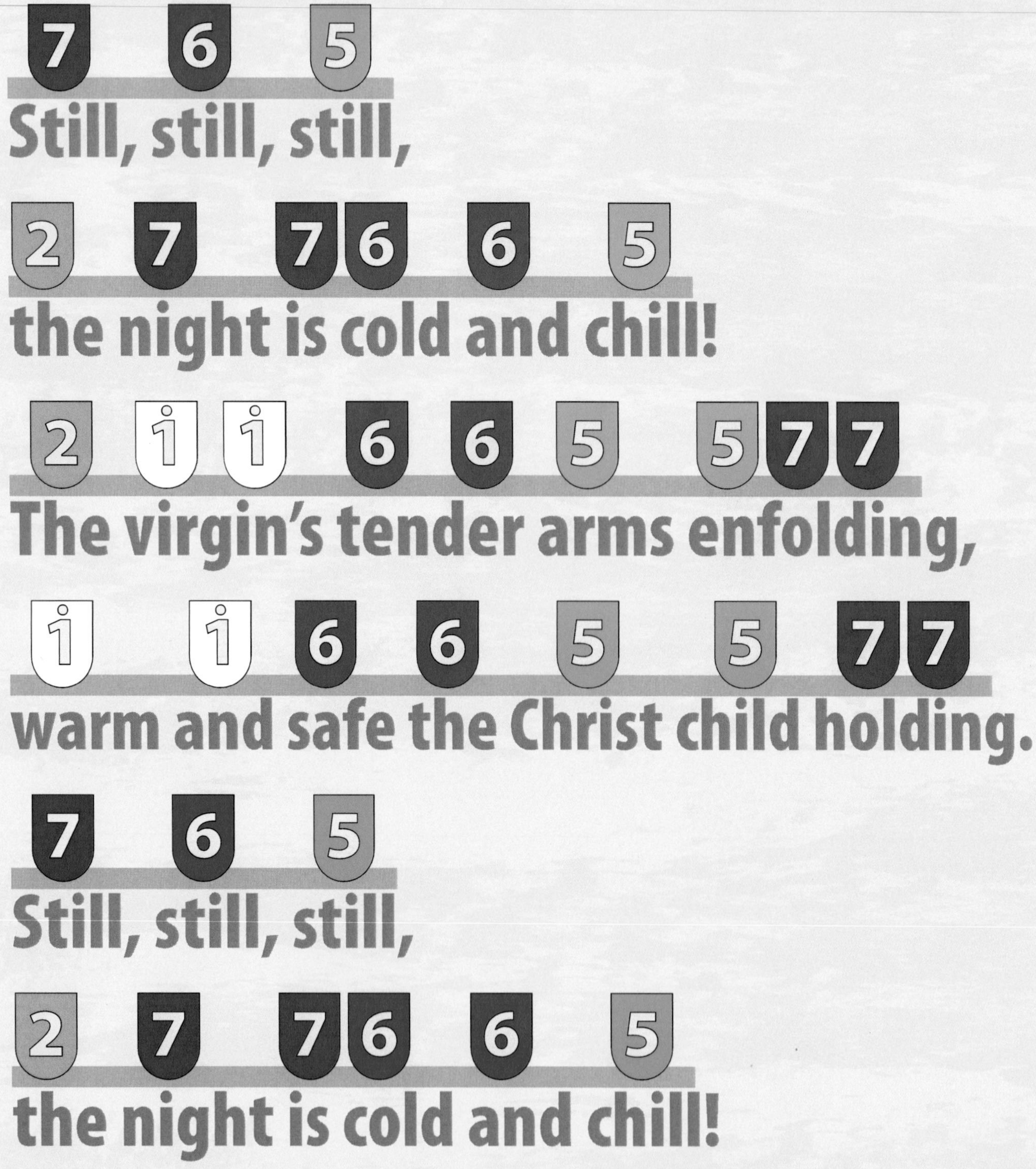

7 6 5
Still, still, still,

2 7 76 6 5
the night is cold and chill!

2 1̇ 1̇ 6 6 5 577
The virgin's tender arms enfolding,

1̇ 1̇ 6 6 5 5 77
warm and safe the Christ child holding.

7 6 5
Still, still, still,

2 7 76 6 5
the night is cold and chill!

Angels we have heard on high

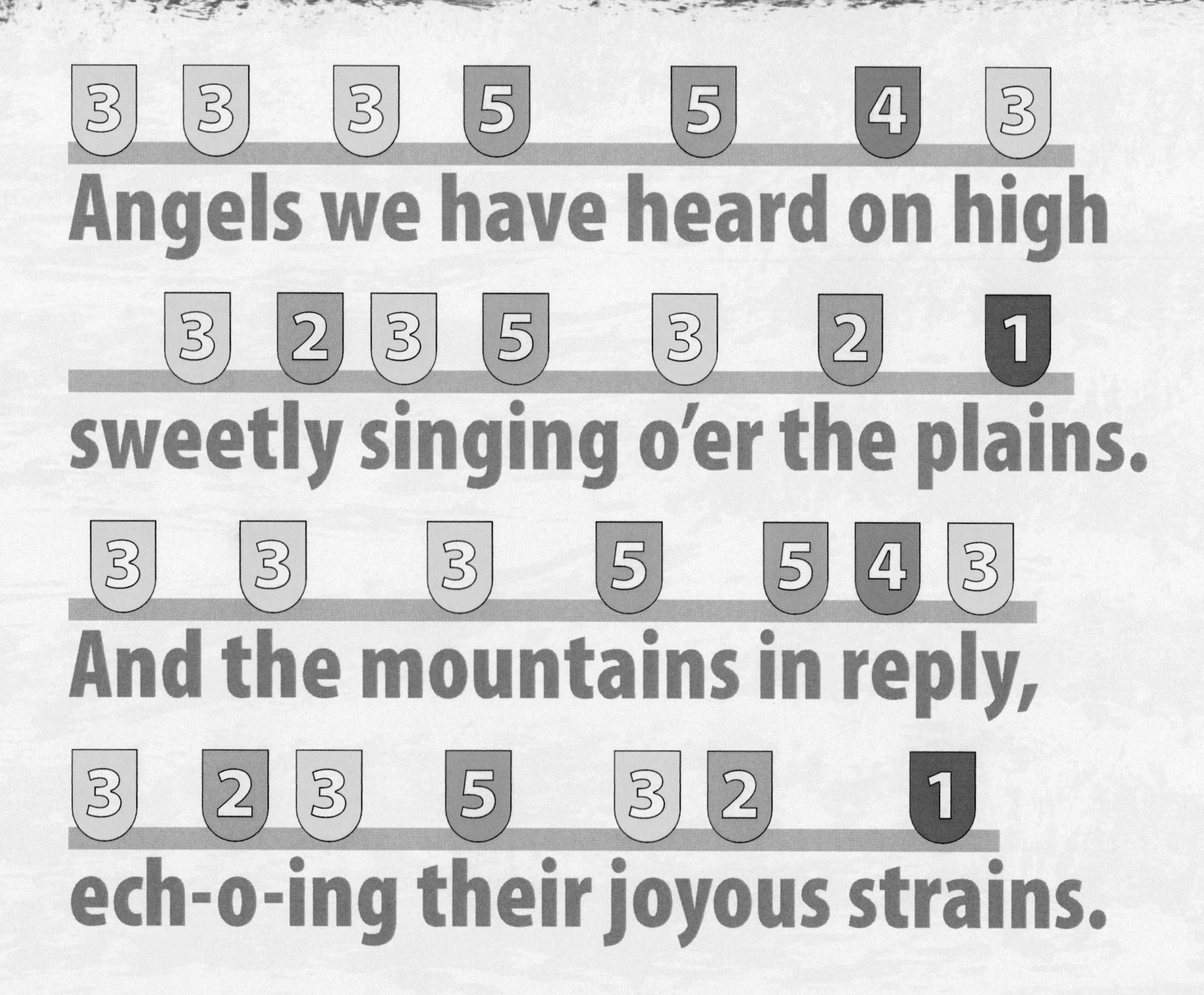
3 3 3 5 5 4 3
Angels we have heard on high
3 2 3 5 3 2 1
sweetly singing o'er the plains.
3 3 3 5 5 4 3
And the mountains in reply,
3 2 3 5 3 2 1
ech-o-ing their joyous strains.

Hark! The herald angels sing

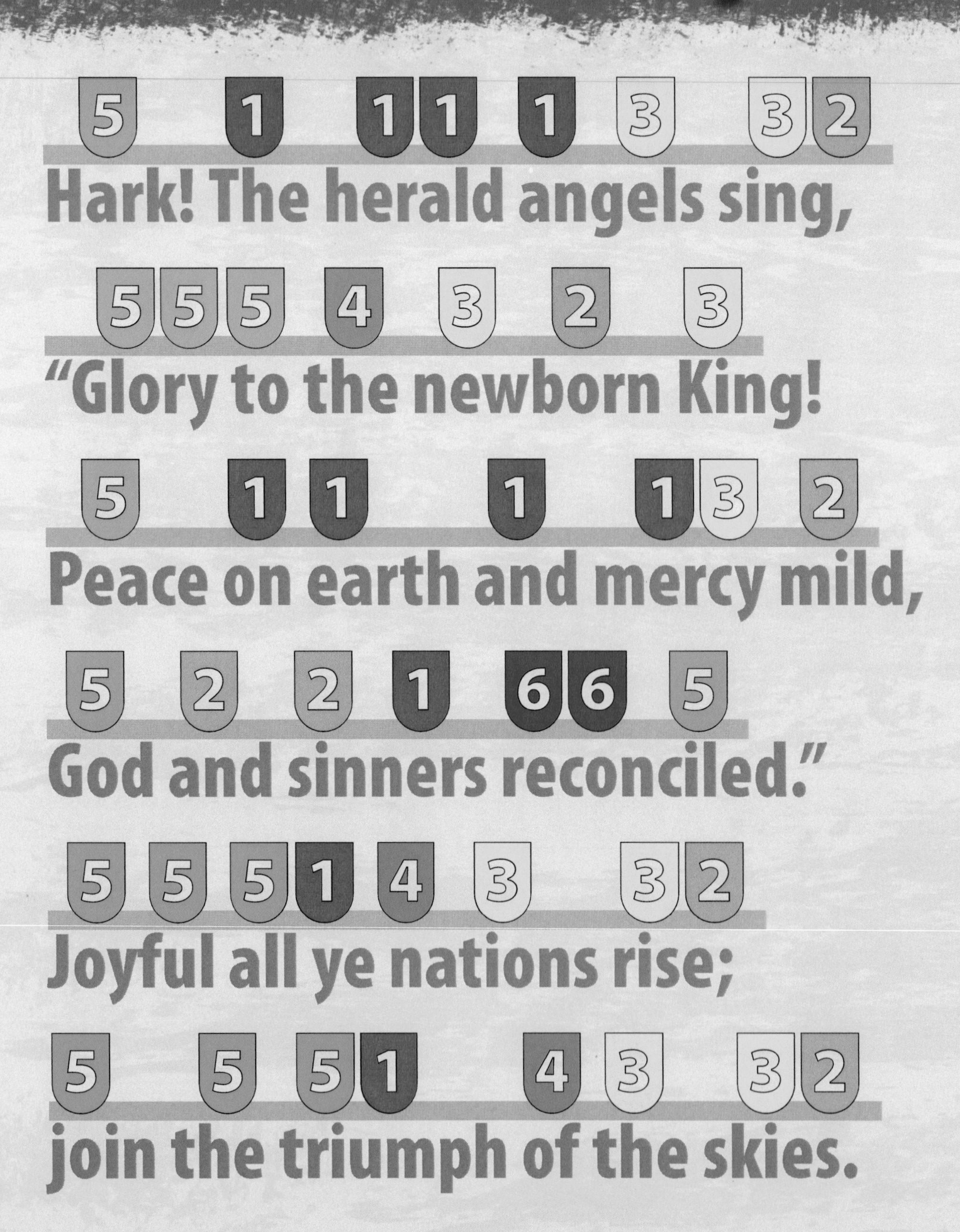
5 1 1 1 1 3 3 2
Hark! The herald angels sing,
5 5 5 4 3 2 3
"Glory to the newborn King!
5 1 1 1 1 3 2
Peace on earth and mercy mild,
5 2 2 1 6 6 5
God and sinners reconciled."
5 5 5 1 4 3 3 2
Joyful all ye nations rise;
5 5 5 1 4 3 3 2
join the triumph of the skies.

6 6 6 5 4 3 2

With angelic host proclaim:

2 3 4 5 1 1 2 3

"Christ is born in Bethlehem."

6 6 6 5 4 3 4

Hark! The herald angels sing,

2 3 4 5 1 1 2 1

"Glory to the newborn King!"

Jesu, joy of man's desiring

3 4 5 5 4 3 2 2
Jesu, joy of man's desiring,

3 4 5 3 2 3 4 3 2 1
holy wisdom, love most bright.

3 4 5 5 4 3 2 2
Drawn by Thee, our souls aspiring,

3 4 5 3 2 3 4 3 2 1
soar to uncre-at- ed light.

2 3 4 4 3 4 5
Word of God, our flesh

3 2 2
that fashioned,

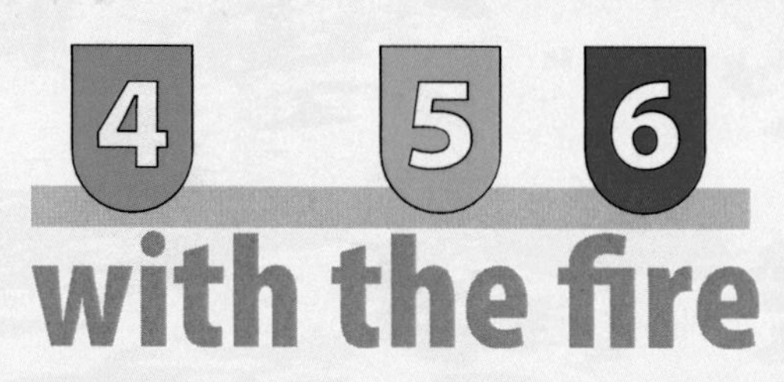
4 5 6

with the fire

6 5 5 4 4

of life impassioned,

3 4 5 5 4 3 2

Striving still to truth unknown,

3 4 5 3 2 3 4

soaring, dying ’round

3 2 1

Thy throne.

It came upon a midnight clear

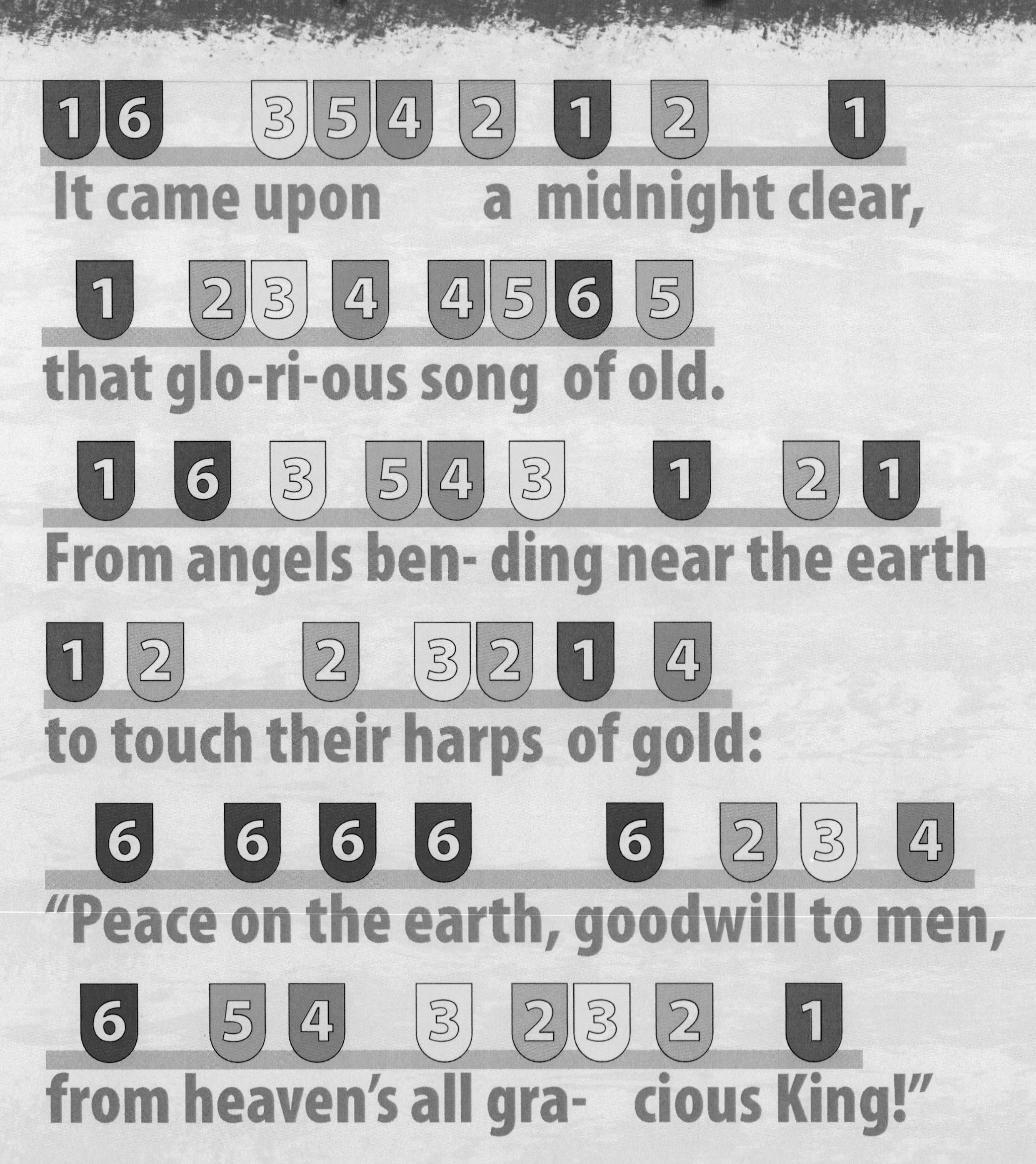

1 6 3 5 4 2 1 2 1
It came upon a midnight clear,
1 2 3 4 4 5 6 5
that glo-ri-ous song of old.
1 6 3 5 4 3 1 2 1
From angels ben- ding near the earth
1 2 2 3 2 1 4
to touch their harps of gold:
6 6 6 6 6 2 3 4
"Peace on the earth, goodwill to men,
6 5 4 3 2 3 2 1
from heaven's all gra- cious King!"

1 6 3 5 4 3 1 2 1

The world in sol- emn stillness lay

1 2 2 3 2 1 4

to hear the an- gels sing.

Jolly old Saint Nicholas

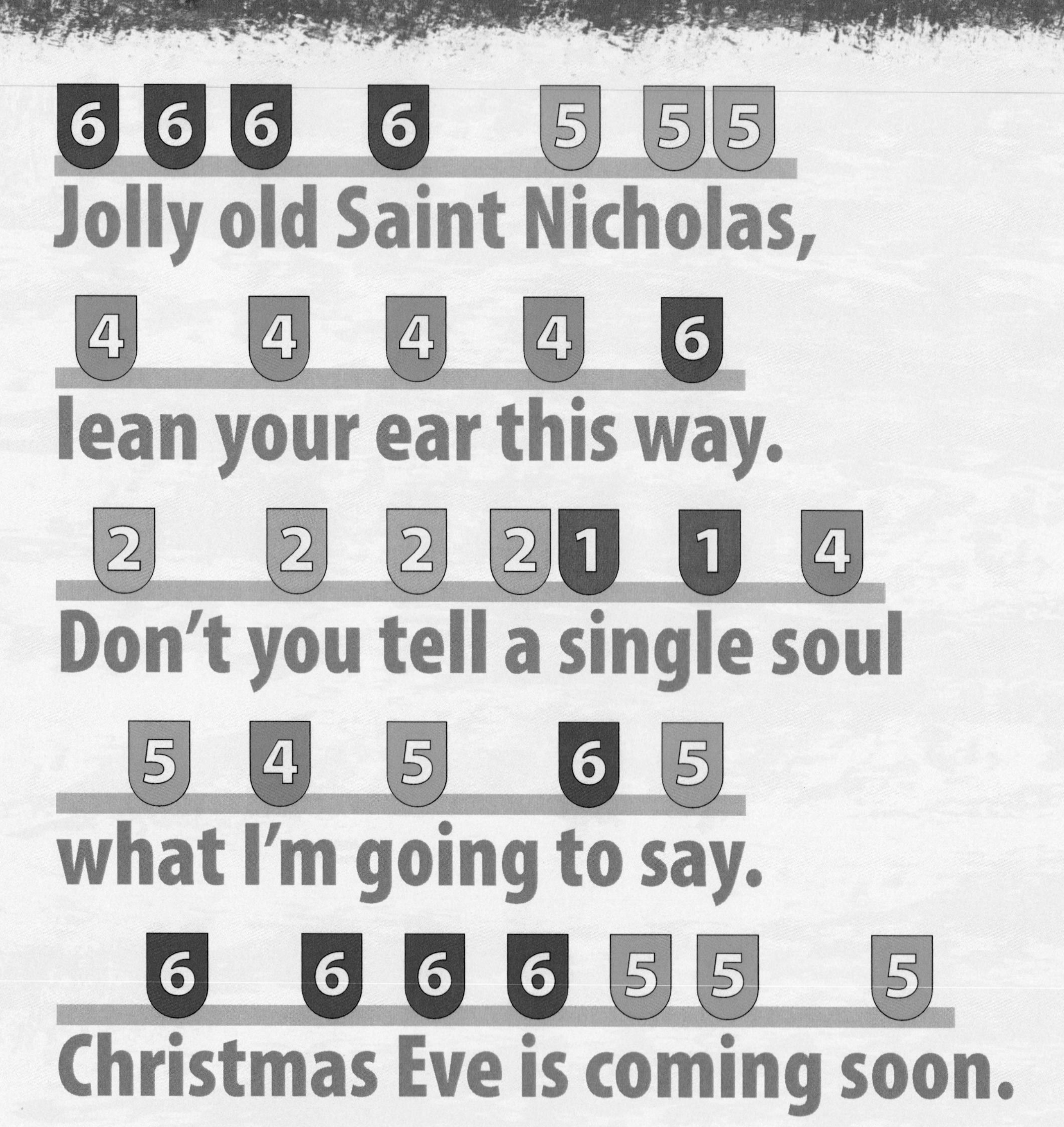
6 6 6 6 5 5 5
Jolly old Saint Nicholas,
4 4 4 4 6
lean your ear this way.
2 2 2 2 1 1 4
Don’t you tell a single soul
5 4 5 6 5
what I’m going to say.
6 6 6 6 5 5 5
Christmas Eve is coming soon.

4 4 4 4 6

Now, you dear old man,

2 2 2 2 1 1 4

whisper what you'll bring to me;

5 4 5 6 4

tell me if you can.

O come, little children

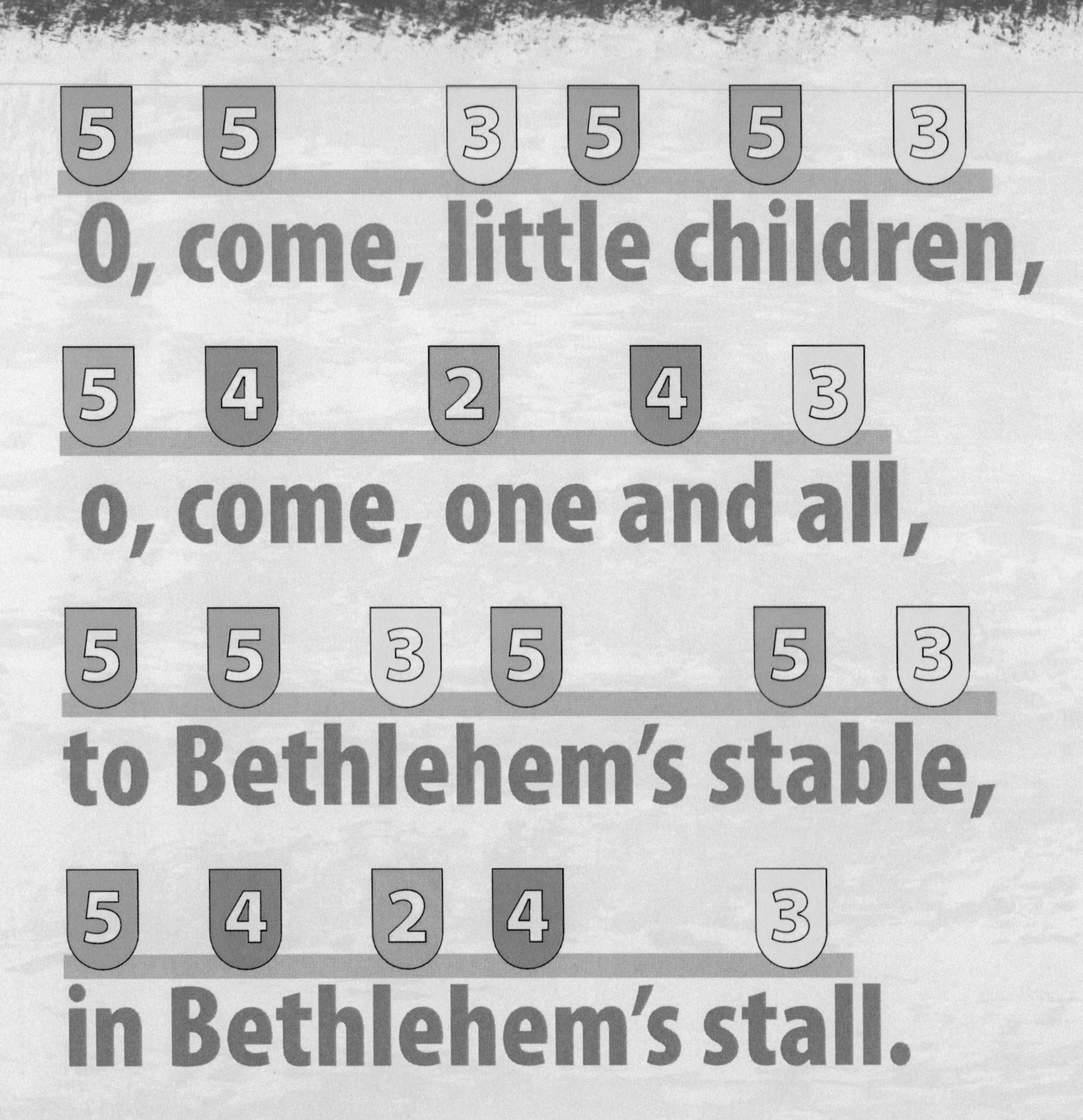
5 5 3 5 5 3
O, come, little children,
5 4 2 4 3
o, come, one and all,
5 5 3 5 5 3
to Bethlehem's stable,
5 4 2 4 3
in Bethlehem's stall.

3 2 2 2 4 4

And see with rejoicing

4 3 3 3 6

this glorious sight,

6 5 5 5 i̇ 5

our Father in heaven

3 5 4 2 1

has sent us this night.

O Sanctissima

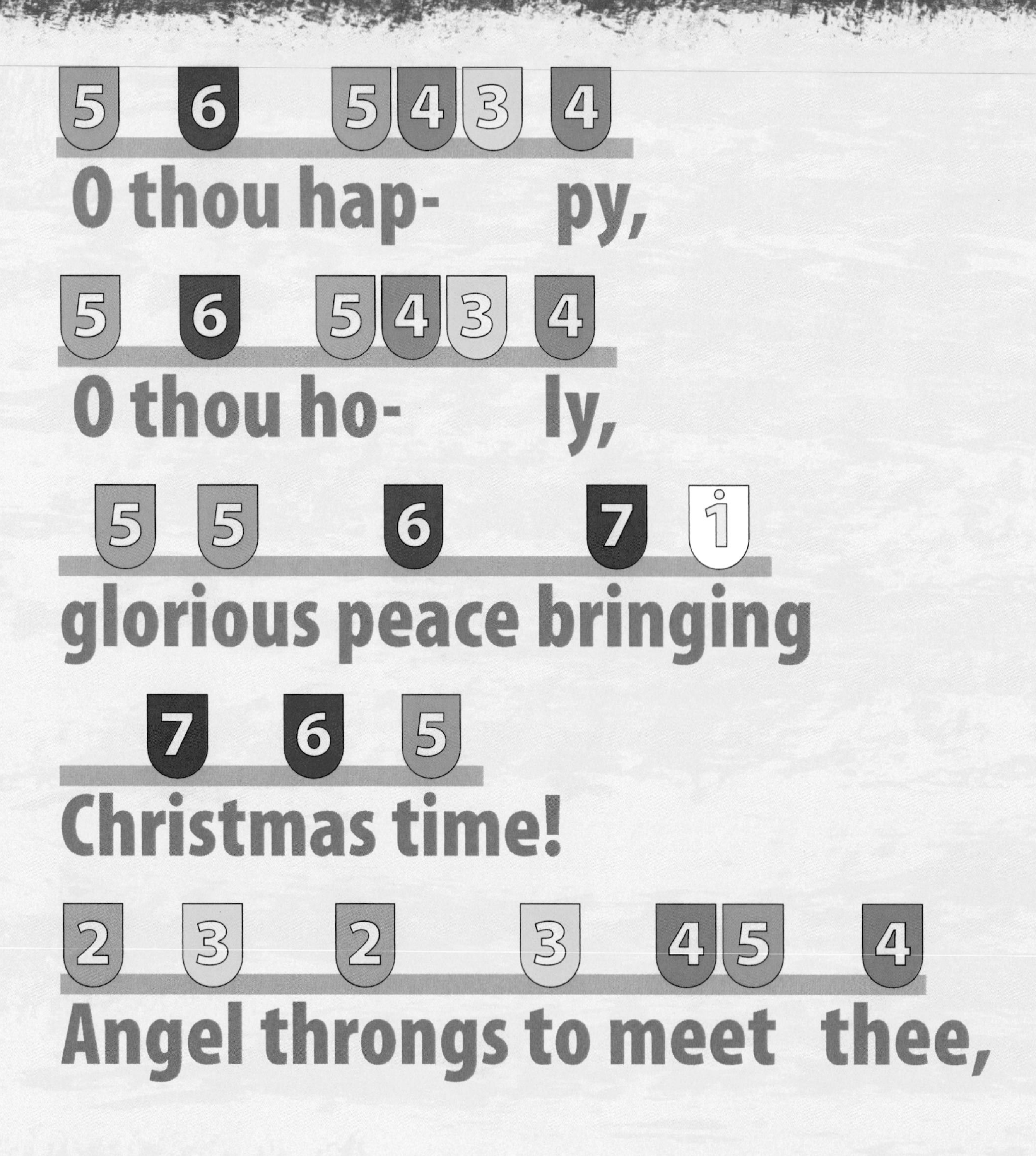
5 6 5 4 3 4
O thou hap- py,
5 6 5 4 3 4
O thou ho- ly,
5 5 6 7 i̇
glorious peace bringing
7 6 5
Christmas time!
2 3 2 3 4 5 4
Angel throngs to meet thee,

2 4 3 4 5 6 5

on Thy birth we greet Thee:

i̇ 7 6 5 i̇ 6 5

Hail to Christ, the Son of God,

4 3 2 1

our newborn king!

While shepherds watched

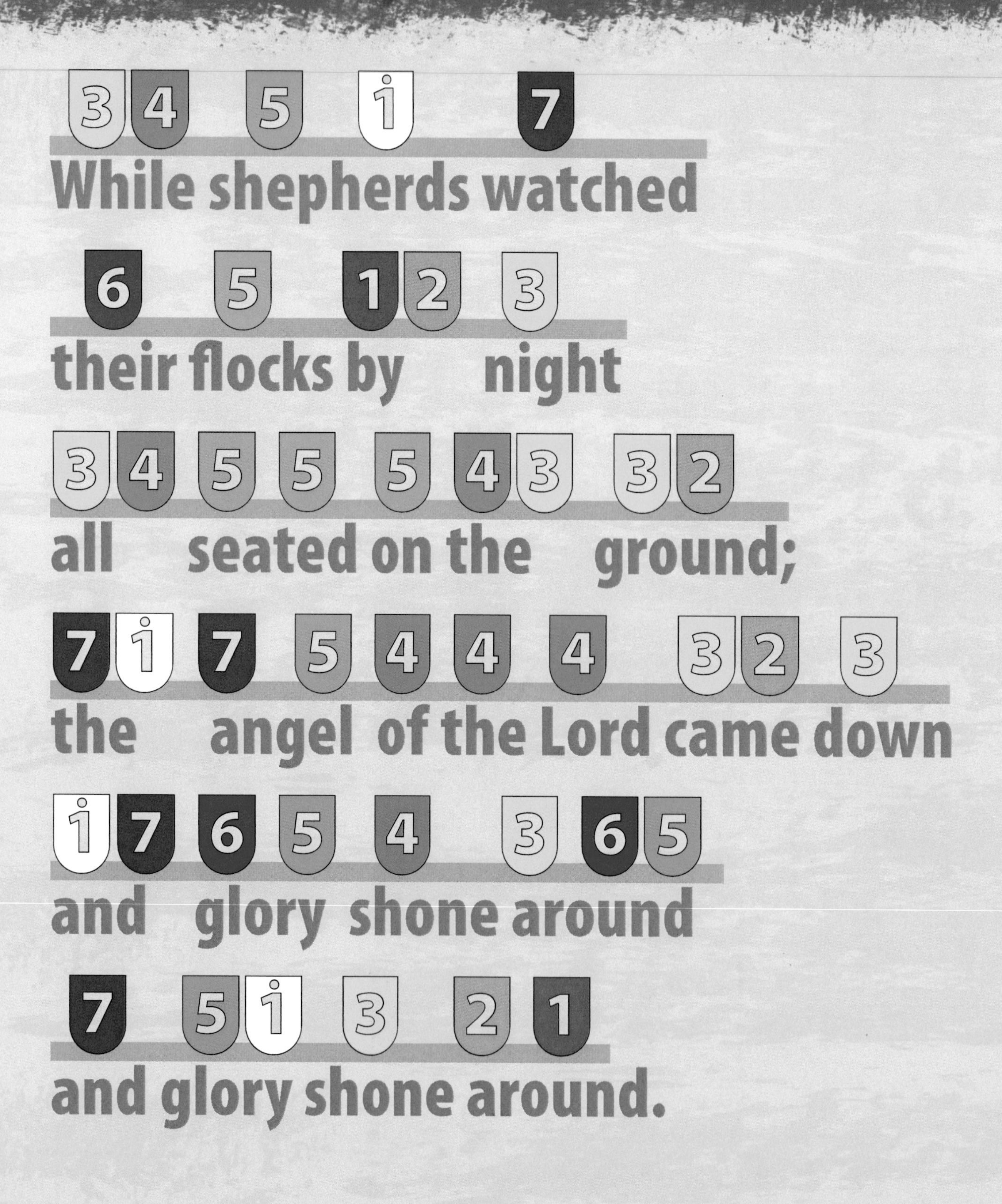

3 4 5 1̇ 7
While shepherds watched
6 5 1 2 3
their flocks by night
3 4 5 5 5 4 3 3 2
all seated on the ground;
7 1̇ 7 5 4 4 4 3 2 3
the angel of the Lord came down
1̇ 7 6 5 4 3 6 5
and glory shone around
7 5 1̇ 3 2 1
and glory shone around.

Labels to fit to your instrument

If you'd rather like to play by colors, cut out these templates (make sure to pick the right size for your kalimba) and fit them to your instrument using a piece of clear adhesive tape.

i 6 4 2 1 3 5 7

10 note model

i 6 4 2 1 3 5 7
i 6 4 2 1 3 5 7
i 6 4 2 1 3 5 7
i 6 4 2 1 3 5 7
i 6 4 2 1 3 5 7
i 6 4 2 1 3 5 7
i 6 4 2 1 3 5 7
i 6 4 2 1 3 5 7

i 6 4 2 1 3 5 7

8 note model

tiny 8 note model

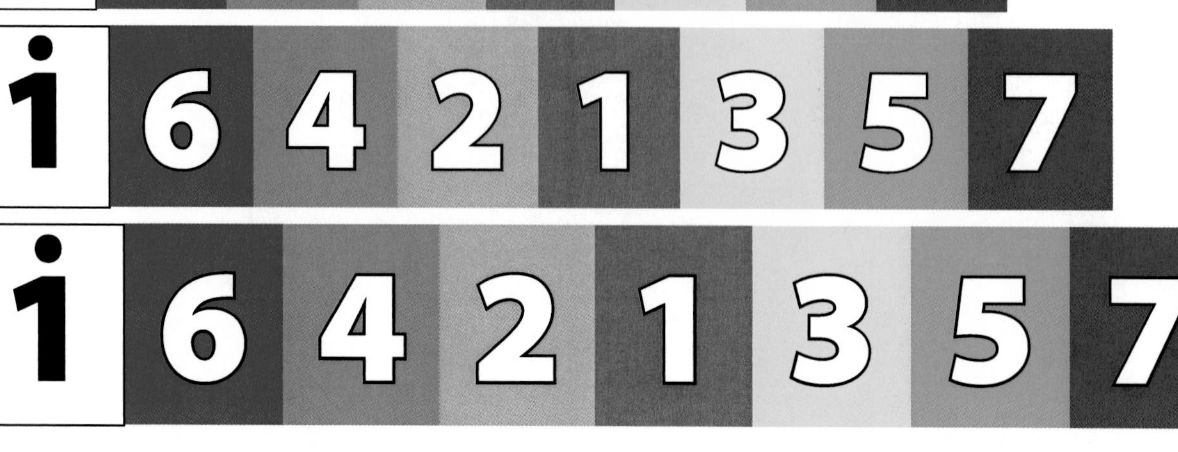
i 6 4 2 1 3 5 7
i 6 4 2 1 3 5 7

Made in the USA
Middletown, DE
16 December 2022

19012586R00022